Dear Parent,

The My First Steps to Reading® series is based on a teaching activity that helps children learn to recognize letters and their sounds. The use of predictable language patterns and repetition of familiar words will also help your child build a basic sight vocabulary. Your child will enjoy watching the characters in the books place imaginative objects in "letter boxes." You and your child can even create and fill your own letter box, using stuffed animals, cut-out pictures, or other objects beginning with the same letter. The things you can do together are limited only by your imagination. Learning letters will be fun—the first important step on the road to reading.

The Editors

My "n" Book

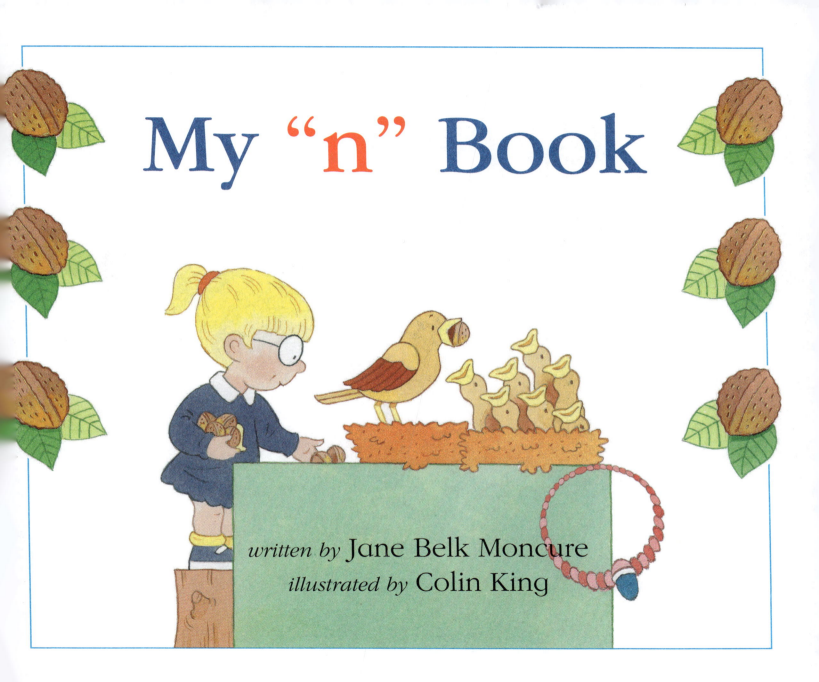

written by Jane Belk Moncure

illustrated by Colin King

Little  had a box.

"I will find things that begin
with my 'n' sound," she said.

"I will put them into my sound box."

Little n found a tree with nuts on it.

Little **n** climbed the tree.
She picked nuts.

How many nuts?

Little  counted nine nuts.

She made the number  .

 Did she put the nuts and the number 9 into her box? She did.

Next, Little  made nine
groups of nuts.

How many nuts?

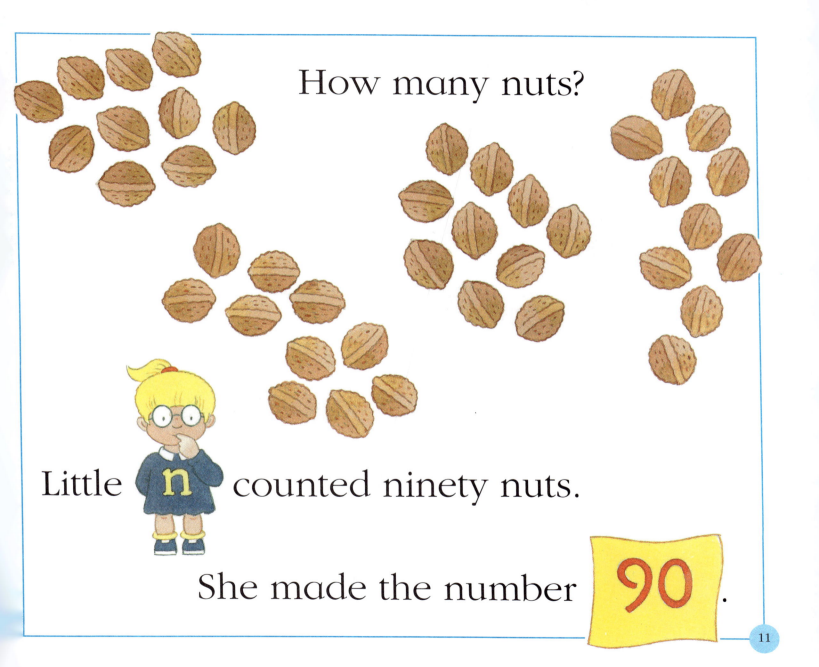

Little n counted ninety nuts.

She made the number 90.

She put these nuts into her box with the other nuts. Now how many nuts did she have?

Little counted ninety-nine nuts.

She made the number **99**.

Did she put the number 99 into her box? She did.

Then Little climbed the tree again.

Little  found nightingales . . .

nine nightingales
eating nuts!

When the nightingales saw

Little **n** ,

they flew into
their nests.

Little  put the nightingales
and their nests
into her box,

carefully . . .

because there were eggs in the nests.

Little  could not count how many.

Little  n was sleepy.

So she took a nap.

The next day, Little  went shopping.

She bought a

necklace

and a
nutcracker.

Little  also bought herself a

nightgown.

Little  carried all her

new things home.

She put on her new nightgown.

Then she heard a noise.
She looked into her box and saw
nineteen new nightingales.

They were crying for nuts!

"Don't cry," said Little 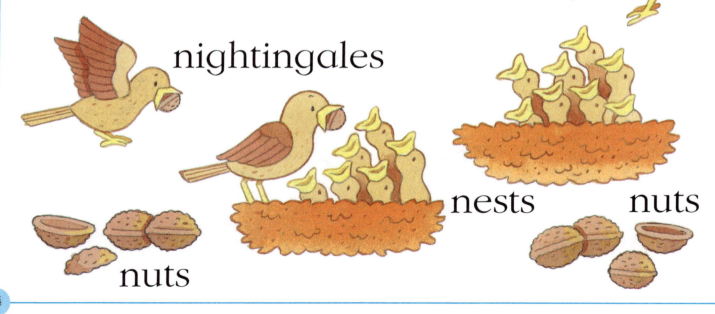 .
"I have enough nuts
for all of you."
She cracked open some nuts.

nightingales

nests

nuts

nuts

While the nightingales
nibbled on nuts,

Little   looked at her
                            new things.

necklace

nightgown   nutcracker

Can you read these words with Little  ?

newspaper

nectarine

noodles

nose

notes

needle

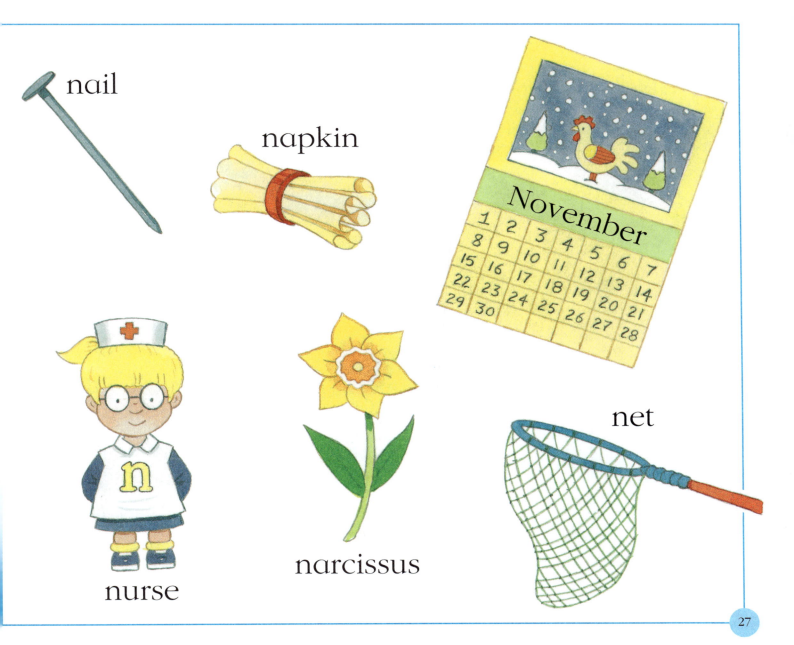

nail

napkin

November

1	2	3	4	5	6	7
8	9	10	11	12	13	14
15	16	17	18	19	20	21
22	23	24	25	26	27	28
29	30					

net

nurse

narcissus

Aa Bb Cc Dd Ee Ff

Nn Oo Pp Qq Rr Ss Tt

My First Steps to READING®